Rookie Read-About® Science

Gator or Croc?

By Allan Fowler

Consultants

Linda Cornwell, Learning Resource Consultant,
Indiana Department of Education

Fay Robinson, Child Development Specialist

Lynne Kepler, Educational Consultant

SCHOLASTIC INC.

New York   Toronto   London   Auckland   Sydney
Mexico City   New Delhi   Hong Kong   Buenos Aires

Project Editor: Downing Publishing Services
Designer: Herman Adler Design Group
Photo Researcher: Caroline Anderson

ISBN 0-439-61810-X

12 11 10 9 8 7 6 5 4 3 2 1   3 4 5 6 7 8/0

Printed in the U.S.A.

First Scholastic printing, October 2003

You know what this fierce–
looking reptile is —an alligator.

Or is it a crocodile?
Here's a quick way
to tell the difference.

If several of its lower teeth
are sticking out when the
animal has its jaws closed . . .
then it must be a crocodile.

crocodile

alligator

When an alligator's jaws
are closed, you can't see
any of its lower teeth.

crocodile

alligator

Also, a crocodile's snout
comes to more of a point
than an alligator's snout.

Both crocodiles (crocs) and alligators (gators) stay in the water much of the time.

alligator

Their long tails whip back and forth, helping them to swim fast.

crocodile

crocodile

Their nostrils and eyes are
on top of their heads, so
they can breathe and see
above water while swimming.

But they can stay under
water a long time without
breathing — as much
as an hour for larger
crocodiles and alligators.

alligators

They live only in places
that are usually warm.

Alligators are found along
the Atlantic coast of the
United States, from North
Carolina to Florida . . .

and in all the states along
the Gulf of Mexico.

alligator

There are alligators in China, too.

Crocodiles live in the Americas, Africa, Asia, and Australia.

Alligators and crocodiles belong to a family of reptiles called crocodilians.

There are two other
kinds of crocodilians —
caimans, in Central
and South America . . .

caimans

gavials

and gavials, in India.

alligator

An alligator might
be about 15 feet long,
but most are smaller.

Some crocodiles have
been known to reach
20 feet or more.

Leathery skin, with thick plates called scales, covers the bodies of crocodilians.

alligator skin

crocodile toes and claws

Their toes are webbed, and
they have claws on their feet.

A female lays dozens of
eggs at a time, about the
size of chicken eggs.

Baby gators or crocs are only 8 to 10 inches long. But they grow fast — about a foot each year for 3 or 4 years, then more slowly.

baby alligators on mother's back

Crocodiles and alligators
like to lie motionless in
the sun for long hours.

crocodile

alligator with fish

They often hunt for food
at night. They eat fish and
shellfish, birds and mammals,
turtles and frogs.

alligator

The croc or gator uses
those strong jaws and
sharp teeth to grip its prey.

It can stun an animal with one swipe of that long tail.

alligator

Alamosaurus   crocodilian

Alligators and crocodiles
are thought to live as
much as 100 years or
more in the wild.

And they have been around
longer than most animals.

When dinosaurs walked the
earth, they had crocodilians
as neighbors.

Yet, human beings came close to killing all the alligators and crocodiles in our country.

Now, laws protect those remarkable creatures.

Crocs and gators deserve to be studied and admired.

But please admire them from a safe distance!

crocodile

Words You Know

Crocodilians

alligator

caimans

crocodile

gavials

nostrils   eyes

snout   teeth

claws   toes   scales

Index

About the Author

Allan Fowler is a free-lance writer with a background in advertising.
Born in New York, he lives in Chicago now and enjoys traveling.

Photo Credits

Photo Researchers Inc. — ©Tom McHugh, cover, 6 (left), 19,
29, 30 (top right), 31 (bottom left); ©David R. Perdew, 6 (right), 30 (top left);
©Root/Okapia/PR, 8; ©M.P. Kahl, 9; ©James Rod/National Audubon
Society, 20; ©J.H. Robinson, 21

SuperStock International, Inc. — ©Gary Neil Corbett, 3; ©Gerard Fritz, 26

Valan Photos — ©Robert C. Simpson, 4, 31 (top); ©Arthur Strange, 7;
©Jeff Foott, 10; ©Stephen J. Krasemann, 12, 25; ©Francis Lepine, 14, 30 (bottom
left); ©Wayne Lankinen, 16-17; ©Phillip Norton, 18, 31 (bottom right); ©Joyce
Photographics, 22

Visuals Unlimited — ©Tom J. Ulrich, 5, 23; ©Ken Lucas, 15, 30 (bottom right);
©David G. Campbell, 24

COVER: Saltwater crocodile, Thailand

Happy Birthday,
Toad

by Elena Rufino
illustrated by Kristin Sorra

 HOUGHTON MIFFLIN BOSTON

Copyright © by Houghton Mifflin Company. All rights reserved.

No part of this work may be reproduced or transmitted in any form or by any means, electronic or mechanical, including photocopying or recording, or by any information storage or retrieval system without the prior written permission of Houghton Mifflin Company unless such copying is expressly permitted by federal copyright law. Address inquiries to School Permissions, Houghton Mifflin Company, 222 Berkeley Street, Boston, MA 02116.

Printed in China

ISBN-13: 978-0-547-02926-9
ISBN-10: 0-547-02926-8

12 13 14 15 0940 20 19 18 17
4500634148

"Today is my birthday,"
said Toad.
"I want to see my
friends."

2

Toad hopped
to Frog's house.
"Hello, Frog!" said Toad.
"Hello," said Frog.

3

cake

"I am making a cake,"
said Frog.
"I like to eat cake,"
said Toad.
"I like cake, too," said Frog.

4

Turtle

Toad hopped
to Turtle's house.
"Hello, Turtle," said Toad.
"Hello," said Turtle.

hats

"I am making hats,"
said Turtle.
"I like hats," said Toad.
"I like hats, too,"
said Turtle.

Toad hopped
to Spider's house.
"Hello, Spider," said Toad.
"Hello," said Spider.

balloons

"I am blowing up
balloons," said Spider.
"I like balloons," said Toad.
"I like balloons, too,"
said Spider.

pond

cake

Toad hopped to the pond.

There were Toad's friends!

Frog had a cake.

Turtle had hats.

Spider had balloons.

9

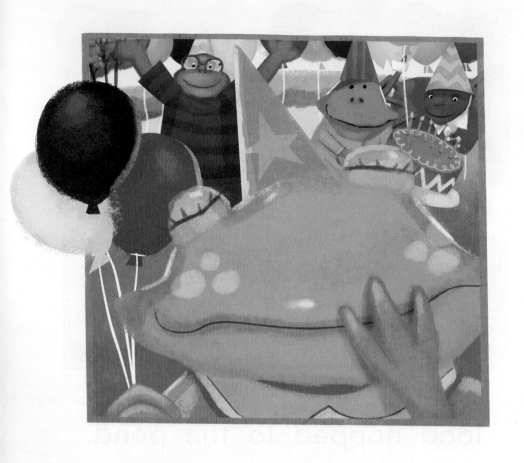

"Happy birthday, Toad,"
said Frog.
"Happy birthday, Toad,"
said Turtle and Spider.

Responding

Story Structure

Who is the story about? Where does the story happen? What happens in the story?
Make a chart.

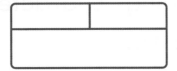

Write About It

Text to Text Think of a story about a party. Who was there? What did they bring to the party? Write two sentences about the party.

11

eat	**put**
give	**small**
one	**take**

✔ **TARGET SKILL** **Story Structure**

Tell the setting, character, and events in a story.

✔ **TARGET STRATEGY** **Visualize**

Picture what is happening as you read.

GENRE A **fantasy** is a story that could not happen in real life.